THE BEST CHRISTMAS EVER!

Junior Discovers Contentment

BY **DAVE RAMSEY**

ILLUSTRATED BY MARSHALL RAMSEY

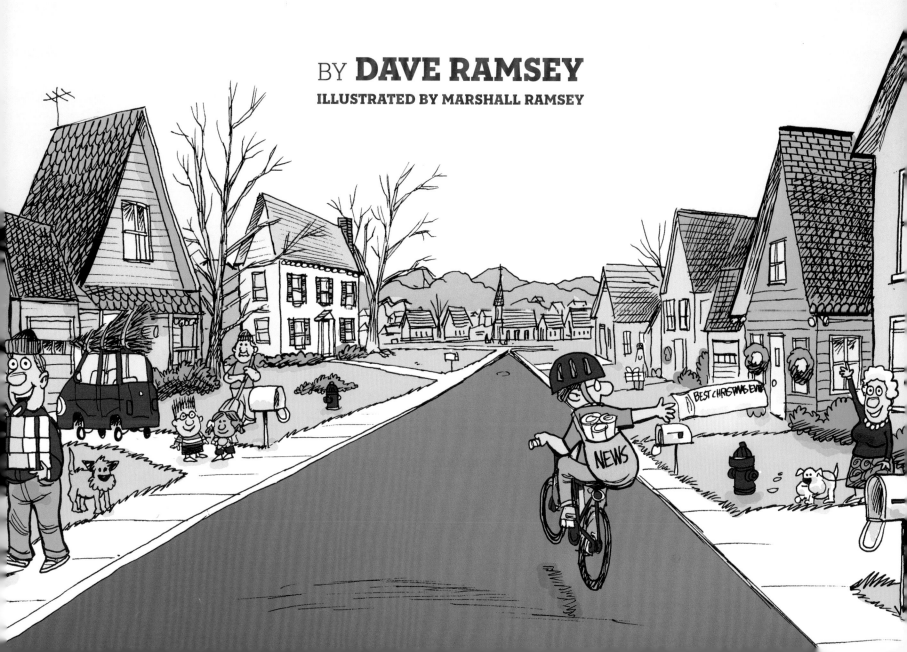

Editors: Christy Wright, Jennifer Gingerich, Darcie Clemen
Cover & interior design: Jason Miller

978-1-937077-50-1
13 14 15 SGC 5 4 3 2

In memory of Granny Bill and Grandpa:

Your love, humor and wisdom can be found
on every page of this book.
Without you, it would be nothing more than
sheets of blank paper.

Thank you and we miss you very much.

Dave and Marshall

Junior, his younger sister, Rachel, and their mom pushed through the crowd of people and into the biggest toy store in town.

Today was the annual Very Merry Toy Bazaar. It took place the first Saturday of December, and every kid in town looked forward to this day all year long.

Welcome! TOYS

5

What they saw inside was magical—giant Christmas trees decorated with candy canes, lollipops, and gingerbread men; enormous ornaments hanging from the ceiling; and toys—

there were **SO** many toys!

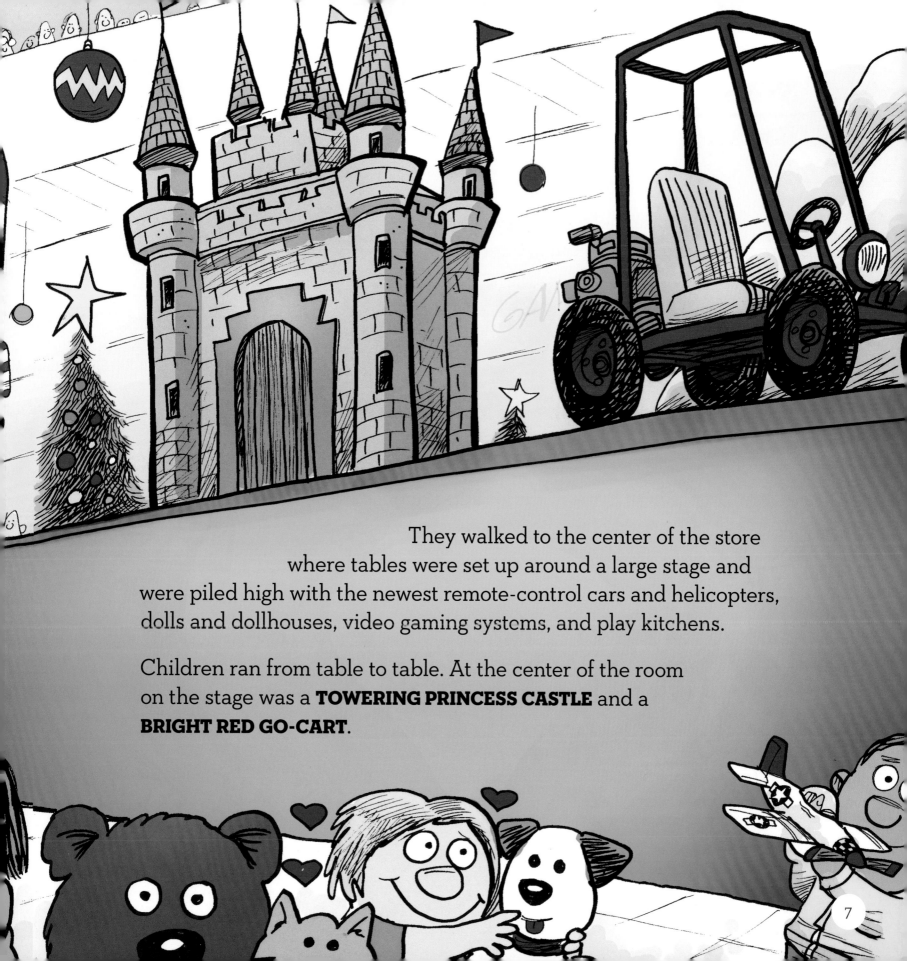

They walked to the center of the store where tables were set up around a large stage and were piled high with the newest remote-control cars and helicopters, dolls and dollhouses, video gaming systems, and play kitchens.

Children ran from table to table. At the center of the room on the stage was a **TOWERING PRINCESS CASTLE** and a **BRIGHT RED GO-CART**.

7

Junior and Rachel were so excited they didn't know where to go first.

They pushed their way to the first table to see two kids wearing virtual-reality gaming goggles—3D goggles that make you feel part of the action when you wear them. A big TV screen over the table showed the players at a life-like race.

Finally, it was Junior and Rachel's turn to play.

They placed the goggles on their heads and saw a 3D running track with hurdles in front of them.

They stood on the start line until they heard,

"Ready, set, GO!"

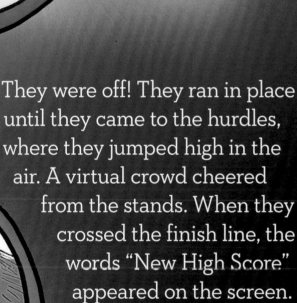

They were off! They ran in place until they came to the hurdles, where they jumped high in the air. A virtual crowd cheered from the stands. When they crossed the finish line, the words "New High Score" appeared on the screen.

They had won!

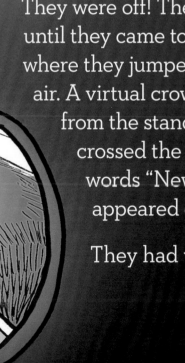

"Did you see that, Mom?!"

Junior asked as he pointed to the screen. "I'm adding the virtual reality gaming goggles to my Christmas list!" He pulled a small notepad and pencil out of his back pocket and made a note.

"Junior, this is just the first toy you've seen," Mom said.

But Junior didn't hear her. He had dashed to the next table.

NEW HIGH SCORE

Just then, a voice turned
their attention to the stage. "Okay, kids.
Only one more hour until we draw the names
of our two Very Merry Toy Bazaar winners. One lucky boy
will win the **REALWHEELS GO-CART**, and one lucky girl will
win the **PRINCESS CASTLE**. If you haven't
signed up, make your way to the
sign-up table."

11

Junior and Rachel raced to the sign-up table and added their names to the drawing.

They'd never won before, but they hoped this would be the year!

BOYS REAL-WHEELS GO-KART

GIRLS PRINCESS CASTLE

SIGN-UP HERE!

Then, they ran through the maze of tables, toys, and kids, **adding nearly every toy to their growing wish lists!** They ran so fast that it was hard to find them in the hustle and bustle of the room!

Finally, the announcer returned to the stage. "Ladies and gentlemen, boys and girls, gather round. It's now time to pick our two lucky Very Merry Toy Bazaar winners. Who will they be?"

"MEEEEEE!" everyone shouted together.

"Let's count down together," directed the announcer.

"Ten, nine..."
Junior couldn't wait to hear his name called.

"Eight, seven..."
In his head, he dreamed of running to the stage.

"Six, five..."
With everyone cheering for him.

"Four, three..."
And climbing into his go-cart.

"Two..."
This was going to be the best Christmas ever!

"One!"

"And now, for the moment you've all been waiting for." The announcer reached into each box, pulled out a piece of paper, and said, "The winners of this year's Very Merry Toy Bazaar contest are . . ."

No one said a word. No one moved.

"Ethan Lee and Olivia Jenkins!"

"Aaaaawww,"
the crowd groaned.

Junior looked at his mom. "I can't believe it. I really thought I was going to win," he cried.

"Me too," Rachel said, tears filling her eyes.

"I know you are disappointed. But winning a contest isn't what makes Christmas special," Mom said. "Come on. It's time to go home."

Junior let out a big sigh and Rachel wiped the tears from her eyes.

18

On the way to the doors, they noticed some simple Christmas trees covered in paper snowflakes. Junior and Rachel stopped to look at them. Each snowflake had something written on it.

Rachel read one snowflake. "Ada, age 5, size small. Needs a coat and gloves. Would like a stuffed dog."

Junior read another. "Jack, age 8, size 10. Needs tennis shoes and long-sleeved shirts. Would like a basketball."

"What's this, Mom?" Junior asked.

GIVE CHRISTMAS TO A CHILD!

SIGN UP HERE

19

"These are called Christmas Children Snowflakes. Some families can't afford to buy gifts at Christmas, so other people buy these children what they want and need."

"You mean some kids don't get new toys for Christmas?" Rachel asked.

"That's right. Some kids are lucky to get even one toy," Mom answered.

"And some kids actually ask for things they need, like new clothes?" Junior asked.

"I know it's hard to understand, Junior, but there are children who need things like coats and gloves," Mom said.

Rachel and Junior were quiet as they thought about this.

"That makes me sad," Rachel said.

"It is sad," Mom agreed. "These snowflakes are a good reminder to be thankful for what we have. They also remind us to help others."

Junior thought about his long Christmas list and about all the toys he already had at home. He was sad that these kids were asking for such simple things. He wanted to help.

And then he had an idea!

"Mom, can I use the money in my GIVE bank to buy Jack what he needs?" asked Junior.

"That's a wonderful idea," Mom said.

"And I want to buy the things on Ada's list!" Rachel said.

"That's great Rachel," said mom as she led them to a sign-up table.

22

Junior and Rachel held their snowflake ornaments tightly as they skipped to the car. On the way home, they talked about shopping for Jack and Ada.

"Hey! I have another idea," Junior announced. "We already have so many toys. Instead of buying new ones this year, what if we make gifts out of things we have at home?"

"That sounds like fun," agreed Rachel.

"It sure does," said Mom. "And we could spend time as a family baking Christmas cookies."

"Oooh, my friend Sarah's family strings popcorn to make garland for their Christmas tree. Can we do that too?" asked Rachel.

"Of course," their mom said.

Back at home, Junior and Rachel began to gather craft supplies, excited about making handmade gifts.

"I'm proud of you both," said Mom. "You are practicing contentment."

"Contentment? What's that?" Rachel asked.

"Contentment is being happy with what you already have instead of focusing on getting or buying more stuff."

"Oh!" Rachel said.

"Yeah," said Junior. "I am happy with what I have."

"Me too," Rachel said. "We have so much. I don't ever want to forget that."

Over the next few weeks, Junior and his family made the most of the Christmas season. They baked cookies, strung popcorn garland for their Christmas tree, watched Christmas movies, and shopped for their Christmas Children. For each other, they created handmade gifts.

When Christmas Eve finally arrived, they gathered in front of the fireplace with mugs of hot chocolate. Dad read the Christmas story and they talked about what the first Christmas Eve might have been like. Junior looked at the presents under the Christmas tree and smiled. He couldn't wait until morning to see what was inside each one.

Before he knew it, it was Christmas morning. Junior and his family ate a huge breakfast and then sat around the Christmas tree to open the gifts they made for each other. Mom passed out the presents.

Dad got a painting from Junior and Rachel to hang in his office. Mom got a calendar made with family photos. Rachel got a bulletin board to hang photos and notes on. And Junior got six different colors of homemade modeling clay.

They spent the rest of the day playing board games around the coffee table.

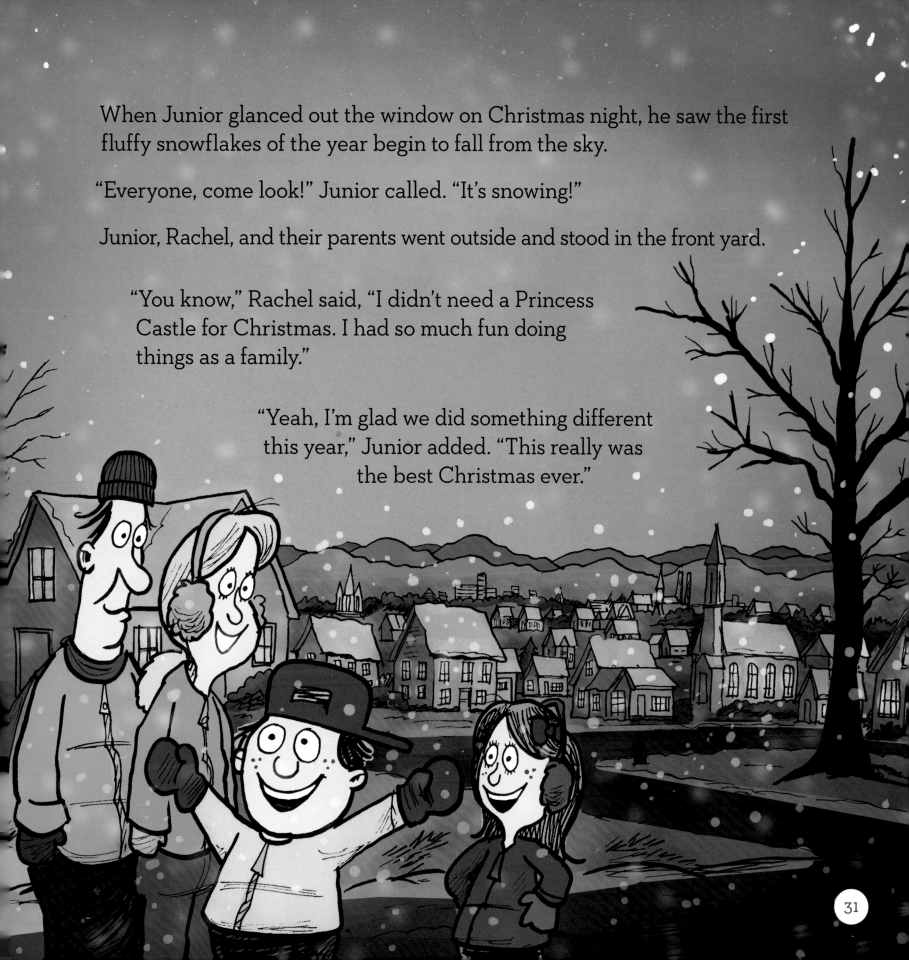

When Junior glanced out the window on Christmas night, he saw the first fluffy snowflakes of the year begin to fall from the sky.

"Everyone, come look!" Junior called. "It's snowing!"

Junior, Rachel, and their parents went outside and stood in the front yard.

"You know," Rachel said, "I didn't need a Princess Castle for Christmas. I had so much fun doing things as a family."

"Yeah, I'm glad we did something different this year," Junior added. "This really was the best Christmas ever."

And it was.

Keep your lives free from the love of money and be content with what you have, because God has said, "Never will I leave you; never will I forsake you."

HEBREWS 13:5

NEW INTERNATIONAL VERSION

Reindeer
cookies

⏱ ABOUT **25-30 MINUTES**

Get more fun and delicious recipes for all occasions at **daveramsey.com/ marthas-place**

INGREDIENTS

- ○ ¹/₂ cup creamy peanut butter
- ○ ¹/₂ cup butter flavor all-vegetable shortening
- ○ ¹/₂ cup granulated sugar
- ○ ¹/₂ cup firmly packed brown sugar
- ○ 1 large egg
- ○ 2 tablespoons milk
- ○ 1 teaspoon vanilla extract
- ○ 1 ³/₄ cups all-purpose flour
- ○ 1 teaspoon baking soda
- ○ ¹/₂ teaspoon salt
- ○ Small bowl of granulated sugar to roll cookies in

Reindeer Decorations

- ○ Large pretzel twists for antlers
- ○ Colorful candy for the reindeer's nose
- ○ Chocolate chips for eyes

DIRECTIONS

1. Preheat oven to 375 F.

2. Cream together peanut butter, shortening, granulated sugar and brown sugar. Add egg, milk and vanilla. Beat well.

3. In separate bowl, stir together flour, baking soda and salt. Slowly add flour mixture to peanut butter mixture. Beat on low speed until stiff dough forms.

4. Shape into 1-inch balls. Roll in sugar. Place 2 inches apart on ungreased cookie sheet.

5. Bake 10 to 12 minutes or until golden brown.

6. Break pretzels in the shape of reindeer antlers. Insert pretzel antlers, candy nose, and chocolate chip eyes into cookies while slightly warm and soft. Let cookies cool completely.

7. Tell the rest of the family they're ready.

8. Enjoy!

HOW TO MAKE: POPCORN GARLAND

 ABOUT **45-60 MINUTES**

WHAT YOU'LL NEED

- ○ Large bowl of stale, butter-free popcorn (3-4 bags, depending on the size of your tree)
- ○ Sewing or embroidery needle
- ○ Embroidery thread or waxed dental floss
- ○ Some patience!

WHAT TO DO

1. Make popcorn the day before to keep it from crumbling. You'll be tempted, but don't eat it!

2. Cut embroidery thread or dental floss in 5-foot lengths.

3. Tie a knot at one end of thread, leaving a 3-inch tail. You'll need that extra length for tying your strands together.

4. Take one strand of thread and push it through the eye of your needle. Three inches is plenty.

5. Then, pinch the two strands together at the eye of your needle with your thumb and forefinger.

6. Push the needle through one kernel of popcorn and drag the popcorn to the knot.

7. Continue threading popcorn onto the thread until you have about three inches remaining.

8. Carefully pull the thread out of your needle and tie a knot to secure the garland. Remember to keep the extra length on the end.

9. Repeat this process until you have enough garland to wrap around your tree.

10. Tie the strands of garland together.

11. Wrap the garland around the tree starting at the top and going around in circles until you reach the bottom. Ask a parent or sibling to help to keep the garland from getting tangled.

12. Sit in front of the tree and admire your hard work! You could celebrate by eating popcorn! With butter!

2 Make popcorn garland

7 Make paper snowflakes

4 Play board games
(Christmas time is family time!)

 9 Make hot chocolate
(Don't forget marshmallows!)

25 Days of Christmas!

25 fun-filled, family activities to make your season bright!

| 1 | 2 | 3 | 4 | 5 | 6 | 7 | 8 | 9 | 10 | 11 | 12 |

8 Set up a nativity scene

3 Have a scavenger hunt of Christmas items

10 Bake Christmas cookies
(Gingerbread's a good idea!)

1 Decorate a Christmas tree

5 Donate old toys and clothes to families in need

11 Adopt a child or family to shop for

6 Build a snowman
(corncob pipe optional)

12 Make handmade gifts for parents and siblings

14 Volunteer at a charity
(food bank, homeless shelter, etc.)

24 Attend a Christmas Eve church service

16 Drive around to see
Christmas lights

20 Put together a puzzle

17 Decorate a
gingerbread house

22 Camp out under the Christmas tree
(or at least next to it)

(13)···(14)···(15)···(16)···(17)···(18)···(19)···(20)···(21)···(22)···(23)···(24)···(25)

19 Watch a Christmas movie

21 Go Christmas caroling

18 Put on a Christmas play

23 Make Christmas pancakes
(Top with red and green sprinkles.)

15 Go sledding
(Snow might help for this one!)

25 Read the
Christmas story
*(Remember why
we celebrate!)*

13 Read Christmas books

A Handmade CHRISTMAS

CREATIVE GIFTS FOR FAMILY OR FRIENDS

SECRET CENTER BOOK

Find an interesting hardback book at home or at a thrift store. Glue the pages together. Then, **with the help of a parent**, cut out a square in the center of the book using a utility knife. This is the perfect gift for hiding little treasures!

DAD & ME OR MOM & ME SKETCH

Draw a simple sketch of your favorite memory with your dad or mom and place it in a nice frame.

BOTTLECAP MAGNETS

Cut small circles from scrapbook paper or magazines and glue to the insides of bottlecaps. You can secure the circles with sealer if you wish. (You can create your own sealer with equal parts glue and water.) Glue a magnet to the back of each bottlecap.

COUPON BOOK

Fold a piece of copy paper in half 3 times. Then unfold and cut the paper on the folds. You should end up with 8 small pieces of paper. Write **"Coupon"** at the top of each piece and decorate the edges. Write a free offer in the center of each coupon (free carwash, free night of babysitting, free garage cleaning, etc.). Make as many coupons as you wish. Stack them and place them in a small gift box. Wrap and tie with ribbon.

PHOTO CALENDAR

With the help of a parent or sibling, choose some of your favorite digital photos and create a photo calendar using a computer. Print and wrap.

ART CARDS

Cut cardstock paper in half, and fold the halves over once to make a card. Paint or draw on the front of your card. Stack 4–8 cards and blank envelopes and tie together with ribbon or string.

MEMORY JAR

Cut 52 strips of colorful construction paper or scrapbook paper. Write a different family memory on each piece of paper. These can be happy, sweet, or even silly. Fold the strips of paper several times and place them all in a jar. Create a label for your jar and finish it off by tying a ribbon around the lid. The recipient will have a memory to read for each week of the year. If you are super ambitious, you could create 365 memories, one for each day of the year.

The Season for Giving

10 Ways to Give at Christmas
(OR ANY TIME OF THE YEAR!)

1 Adopt a child/family to buy Christmas presents for.

2 Deliver a Christmas meal to a needy family.

3 Sing Christmas carols at a nursing home.

4 Take coloring books and crayons to sick children at a hospital.

5 Make your parents breakfast and deliver it to their room.

6 Give candy canes to homeless people in your city or town.

7 Serve lunch or dinner at a homeless shelter.

8 Volunteer at a food bank.

9 Take hot chocolate and cookies to your next-door neighbor.

10 Make handmade cards for an elderly couple in your neighborhood.

The Christmas Story

The Birth of Jesus

LUKE 2:1-20 (NCV)

At that time, Augustus Caesar sent an order that all people in the countries under Roman rule must list their names in a register. This was the first registration; it was taken while Quirinius was governor of Syria. And all went to their own towns to be registered.

So Joseph left Nazareth, a town in Galilee, and went to the town of Bethlehem in Judea, known as the town of David. Joseph went there because he was from the family of David. Joseph registered with Mary, to whom he was engaged and who was now pregnant. While they were in Bethlehem, the time came for Mary to have the baby, and she gave birth to her first son. Because there were no rooms left in the inn, she wrapped the baby with pieces of cloth and laid him in a feeding trough.

Shepherds Hear About Jesus

That night, some shepherds were in the fields nearby watching their sheep. Then an angel of the Lord stood before them. The glory of the Lord was shining around them, and they became very frightened. The angel said to them, "Do not be afraid. I am bringing you good news that will be a great joy to all the people. Today your Savior was born in the town of David. He is Christ, the Lord. This is how you will know him: You will find a baby wrapped in pieces of cloth and lying in a feeding box."

Then a very large group of angels from heaven joined the first angel, praising God and saying: "Give glory to God in heaven, and on earth let there be peace among the people who please God."

When the angels left them and went back to heaven, the shepherds said to each other, "Let's go to Bethlehem. Let's see this thing that has happened which the Lord has told us about."

So the shepherds went quickly and found Mary and Joseph and the baby, who was lying in a feeding trough. When they had seen him, they told what the angels had said about this child. Everyone was amazed at what the shepherds said to them. But Mary treasured these things and continued to think about them. Then the shepherds went back to their sheep, praising God and thanking him for everything they had seen and heard. It had been just as the angel had told them.